FIDDLE MUSIC FRO

The 18th century Scottish music collections of

ALEXANDER LEBURN, Auchtermuchty
and JAMES WALKER, Dysart

PUBLISHED IN 2006 BY

HIGHLAND
MUSIC
TRUST

Arras, Drumossie, Inverness IV2 5BB, Scotland
Tel. 01463 717811 Email hmt@heallan.com
www.heallan.com

ISMN M 708062 004

Music set by Helen Allan   Project managed by Eric Allan
Advisers: Duncan Dyker, Charles Gore, Douglas Muir,
George Penman, Alastair Robertson

Printed in Scotland by Dingwall Printers Ltd
Cover illustration from an early 20th century painting
of Dysart Harbour, by courtesy of the Dysart Trust

HIGHLAND MUSIC TRUST is a Scottish charity, no. SC028065, established for the
advancement of education in and knowledge of Scottish national and traditional music.
Profits on the sale of this book will be used to continue the work of the Trust in making music
available to all.

CONTENTS
INTRODUCTIONS
INDEX

FROM THE PUBLISHERS

Eric & Helen Allan

This book is the result of a happy collaboration, initiated by an article in the June 2004 Box and Fiddle magazine by George Penman, accordionist and retired pharmacist from Kirkcaldy. George wrote of the concern he shared with his fellow-townsman and school crossing controller Alastair Robertson and musician Douglas Muir, that the music of two great Fifers had not been made available to all. Responses from Charlie Gore and ourselves led to correspondence and sharing of information and to the eventual appearance of this book.

We have edited the tunes as little as possible, restricting ourselves to detail of musical notation. We decided to include the bass lines, although some are rudimentary, and we have edited them lightly where the lack of harmony suggests errors in the original printing.

We gratefully acknowledge the support of the Scottish Arts Council, Fife Council and Cambridge Scottish Society and their Dance Group towards this publication, and thank Charlie Gore, George Penman, Alastair Robertson, Douglas Muir and Duncan Dyker for their enthusiasm and expertise, and George for the excellent photographs of Auchtermuchty and Dysart..

THE COMPOSERS

(from the notes of George Penman and Alastair Robertson)

Alastair Robertson and George Penman

Our two composers were contemporaries, living in the same county, both enjoying the patronage of the landed gentry, and both incidentally sharing the same publisher, James Johnson, who also published the songs of Robert Burns. But their circumstances were otherwise quite different.

Alexander Leburn (1767 – 1836) was born and died in the Royal Burgh of Auchtermuchty, where, according to Piget's "Scotland – 1825-26", he was engaged in the trade of druggist. He was a magistrate of the burgh, and, in the words of his obituary, "a self taught philosopher of no mean order" with "considerable proficiency in mathematics, chemistry, astronomy and general science". His mathematical ability led to the invention of the Leburn Optical Square, a measuring instrument for surveyors. He played on an Italian violin gifted to him by the Earl of Leven.

James Walker (1760 –1840), from the Royal Burgh of Dysart, on the other hand, was a full-time musician and teacher, much in demand for grand balls and dancing parties, but also accustomed on these occasions to giving the servants below stairs a session of music. Many of his tunes are named after local beauty spots. He was buried in the churchyard of St Denis, near to a 16th century Blackfriars priory. The site is now a children's playground, where we can imagine the young people skipping to a heavenly reel by "Auld Jeems Walker".

THEIR PLACE IN SCOTTISH MUSIC

Charles Gore

During the adult lives of the two stalwarts whose work is featured in this book the Gows were flourishing in Athole and Edinburgh, William Marshall on Speyside and scores of other fiddler-composers found themselves in demand. All manner of people were dancing ecstatically, the better-off in their ballrooms and town drawing-rooms, the less well-off in the farm towns and on the village green. From the far north to the Borders it was truly the Golden Age of the fiddler and his music and there was always a cry for more.

Alexander Leburn of Auchtermuchty was a self-taught musician, a first-rate mathematician and public figure. His obituary in the *Fifeshire Journal* - "...unostentatious, his heart kind, his integrity incorruptible ...much respected by all ranks..." could so easily have been written in praise of a famous 20th century son of the Royal Burgh, the late Sir Jimmy Shand. Rossie House, Mugdrum, Myres Castle - all within a mile or so of the town - and other local houses get mention in titles and Leburn includes several pieces "By a Lady" (names were sometimes excluded out of delicacy!). He dedicated his 1793 collection to Mrs. Moncrieff of Reedie (whose estate lay between Auchtermuchty and Strathmiglo), and several of the individual tunes to members of the family.

James Walker of Dysart published his two volumes of music in about the years 1795 and 1799 (both are undated). As a music teacher and bandleader, he was drawn into the social life of the burgh and dedicated his first volume to the Master and Brethren of the Masonic Lodge. Patronage was an established means of support for musicians in that age. There was no safety net for a musician who left a widow and children. So patrons and their families were rewarded with tune titles. The subscribers' list for the first volume of Walker's music numbered 200. A glance down the index shows how patronage was acknowledged, with Sir James Erskine St. Clair (the "Right Worshipful Master") and his family in pole position. Not far away, Balcarres Castle was full of the sound of music (the lady of the house was herself a talented composer of dance tunes). Dunnikeer (Dunnikier) House (a slow strathspey) was home of a family of Oswalds and there were several other families with musical interests.

Another of Fife's musical sons, James Oswald, born in Crail about 1710 and for a while a dancing-master in Dunfermline, was author of many publications in the period just before the great age of dance. His "Caledonian Pocket Companion" (15 volumes, 1746-59) is a tune source of real value. By the 1760s, Oswald had moved to Edinburgh, then to London where he was appointed "Chamber Composer" to the King.

THE MUSICIAN'S VIEW

Douglas Muir

When Alastair Robertson sent me photocopies of these collections, my initial interest was in the fact that both composers were from Fife, an area not much represented in the traditional fiddle music of Scotland. I suppose I presumed that the quality of the tunes would be unremarkable – else why would these composers not be better known today? It was with surprise and considerable satisfaction that I found that these collections contain many excellent tunes that I knew I would want to include in dance sets for the band.

For a start, many are simply great tunes in themselves – such as the strathspey *Dysart House* or the jig *Miss Abercrombie's Fancy*, both bright in melody and colourful in harmonic structure. In addition, both composers offer a wide range of keys through sharps and flats, major and minor, enabling the construction of dance sets with variety of tone and mood. And as a teacher of Scottish accordion I will happily use many of these tunes because, in addition to being satisfying to play, they are challenging for both the right and left hands of the instrument – tunes like *Mrs Cunningham of Bonnington's Strathspey* and *Miss Catherine Miller's Reel.*

I would strongly recommend Scottish dance bands and traditional players to plunder these collections and enrich their repertoire.

Douglas Muir began playing accordion at the age of 8, and, having bought a new accordion in his early twenties, started playing Scottish dance music to help pay for it. In 1963 he joined what was eventually to become known as John Ellis and the Highland Country Band, with whom he has made countless recordings, broadcasts and overseas trips. Since 1981 he has taught in music summer schools at Stirling University, Queen Margaret College, Edinburgh and St Leonard's, St Andrews.

Duncan Dyker has been a valuable member of the Highland Music Trust "team" in the production of several major collections, advising, proof reading and performing at launches and presentations. Born in Huntly, where he received a good grounding in both fiddle and pipes (and incidentally had Douglas Muir as his English teacher) Duncan has excelled as a solo fiddler, winning major championships, and is leader of Inverness Fiddlers, a member of the group BIRL and a fiddle maker. He recently recorded a CD *Collectors' Items* for Highland Music Trust, featuring music from the great fiddle collections.

INDEX

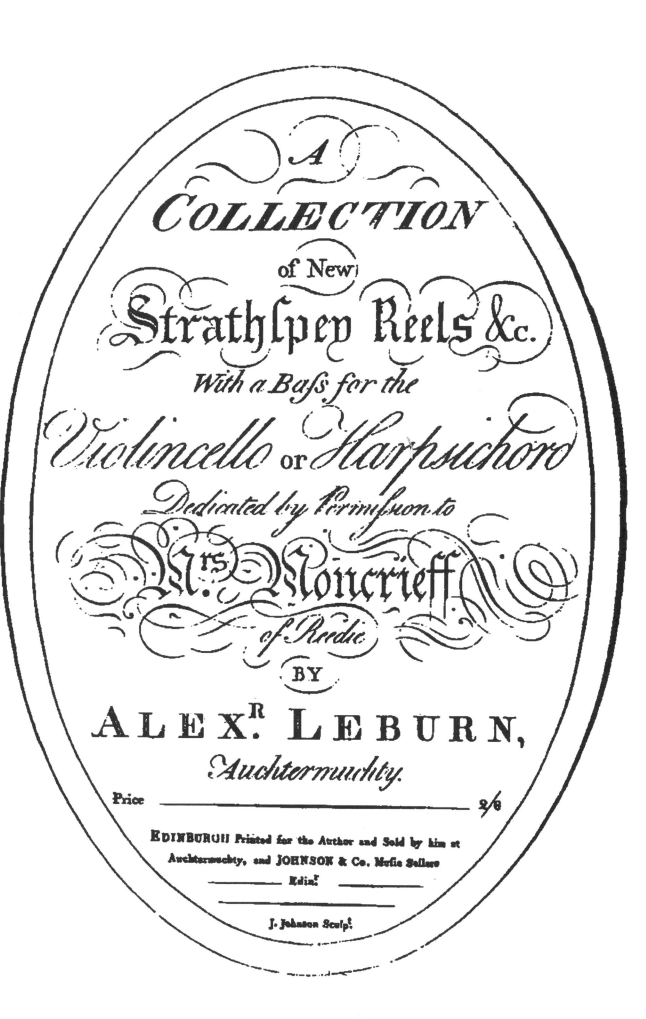

A

COLLECTION

of New

Strathspey Reels &c.

With a Bass for the

Violincello or Harpsichord

Dedicated by Permission to

Mrs Moncrieff

of Reedie

BY

ALEXR. LEBURN,

Auchtermuchty.

Price ——————————————— 2/6

EDINBURGH Printed for the Author and Sold by him at
Auchtermuchty, and JOHNSON & Co. Music Sellers
———— Edinr. ————

J. Johnson Sculpt.

The Myres Castle   a Reel

Mrs Moncrieff of Reedie's Delight   a Strathspey

Miss Moncrieff of Reedie's Strathspey

Honbl George Melvill Leslie Melvill's Strathspey

Mugdram House

a Reel

Steuart Lodge

a Strathspey

Miss Spiers's Jigg

Miss Lindsay Steuart of Steuart Lodge's Strathspey

Pitlower Harmitage

4

Miss Steuart of Steuart Lodge's Reel

Honble Miss Ruthven's Reel

By a Lady

5

Henry McLiesh's Complements to A Leburn

H McLiesh

Miss Margret Steuart of Steuart Lodge's Reel

Lady Elisabeth Moncreiffe's Reel

Mrs Duncan's Reel

Honble Miss Jessie A Ruthven's Strathspey

Miss Caroline Thomson's Reel

Lady Jane Dundas's Reel

By a Lady

Pitlower House

A reel

Mrs Cheape of Rossie's Strathspey

Miss Moncrieff of Pitlower's Reel

Miss Dalzell's Strathspey

Miss Belsches's Strathspey

Slowish

Patrick George Moncrieff Esqr of Reedie's Jigg

11

Honble Miss Ruthven's Strathspey

Slow

Miss Hay of Lyes's Strathspey

12

Honble Miss Jane Ruthven's Jigg

Mrs Kelty Auchtermuchty's Favourite

Brisk

The Cuckoo

A favourite Irish Jigg

Slowish

Miss Belsche's Whim

by A Lady

Honble Miss Jessie A Ruthven's Favourite

by A Lady

Slow

Miss Abercrombie's Fancy

by A Lady

Slow

Mrs Cunningham of Bonningtone's Strathspey

Slow

Lady Jane Belsches's Alamande

by A Lady

Honble George Melvill Leslie's Alamande

by A Lady

Miss Pillans's Strathspey

by A. J.

17

Statue of Sir Jimmy Shand, Auchtermuchty

A
COLLECTION
of New

Scots Reels, Strathspeys, Jigs, &c.

With a Bass for the

Violincello or Harpsichord

Dedicated to the Right Worshipful Master

Sir James Erskine St. Clair,

of Sinclair, Bart

& the Worthy Brethren of the free Mason Lodge in Dysart.

BY

JAMES WALKER,

Price ———————————— 3/

Printed for the Author and to be had at his house
in Dysart. — Sold also by JOHNSON & Co.
Music Sellers Lawn Market EDINBURGH.

J. Johnson Sculpt

Sir James St Clairs March

Lady St Clair Dysarts Strathspey

Miss Reddies Reel

Ralph's Frolick   a Reel

Miss Rutherford Kinghorn's Strathspey

Lady Erskine's Reel

McLean's Bonny Lassie

Miss Barclay's Reel

Miss Catherine Miller's Reel

Miss Charlotte Stirlings Reel

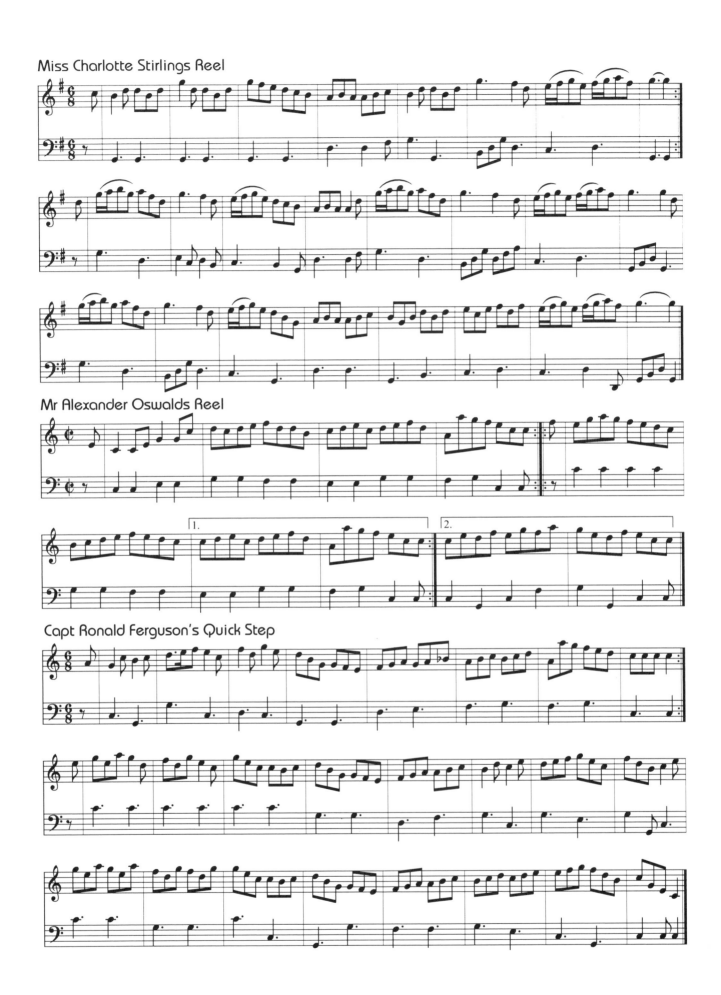

Mr Alexander Oswalds Reel

Capt Ronald Ferguson's Quick Step

Mr Oswalds of Dunnikier's Reel

Dunnikeer House

Slow

Miss Jessy Wallace Reel

By R Wallace

Walker's Favourite

by Mr Jas. Henderson

Miss Ferguson of Reith's Strathspey

Dysart House Strathspey

Miss Wemyss of Dundee's Reel

Kirkcaldy Merchant's Hall   a Reel

A March

Miss Margt St Clair Reddies Fancy

Mr David Duncan's Reel

Miss Willes of Leslies Birthday

by A Dempster

Mr James Belfour's Fancy

27

Capt James Abercrumbie's Reel

Miss Elezbath Oswald's Reel

Miss Jean Donaldson's Hornpipe

Mr John Walker's Favourite

Wemyss Castle Reel

29

Mr John Dykes Reel

Miss Mar. Marshalls Scotch Measure

by H McLiesh

30

Dysart Masson Lodge Harmony

Quick Step

Slowish

31

Miss Erskine of Tory's Strathspey

Mrs Reas Reel

Mrs Melvill Dysart Reel

Gooden Well   or   Mr Buist's Frolic   a Reel

The Honourable Miss Francess Hay's Quick Step

Honourable Miss Francess Hay's Reel

Mr John Reddie's Strathspey

Dunnikier House

Dysart Harbour

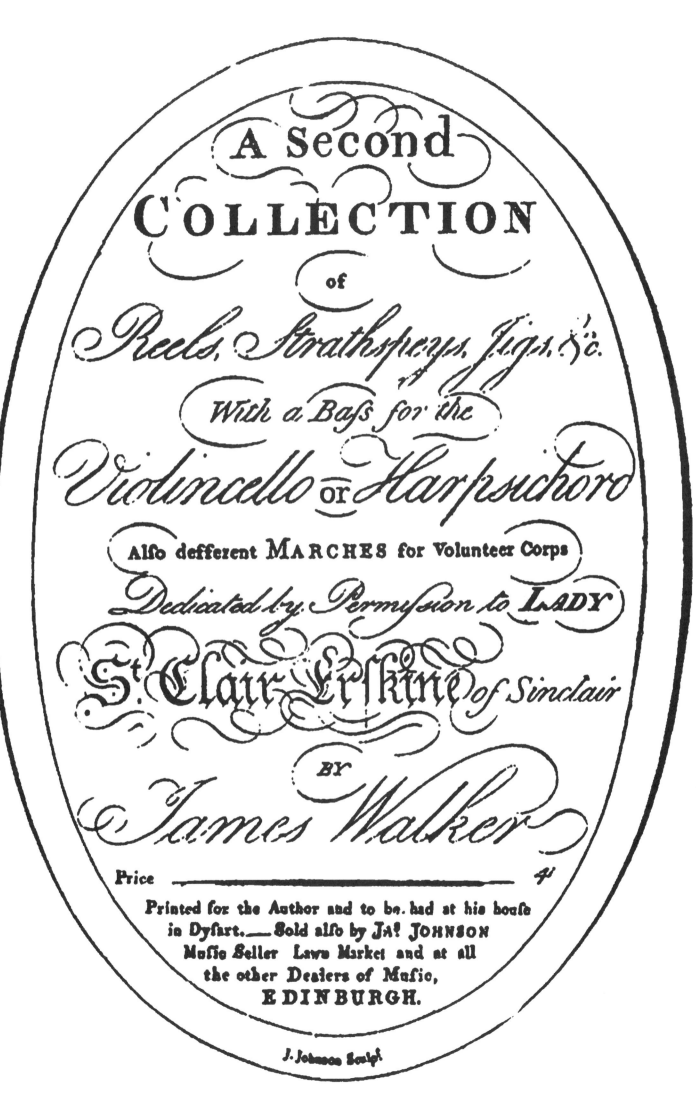

A Second
COLLECTION
of
Reels, Strathspeys, Jigs, &c.
With a Bass for the
Violincello or Harpsichord
Also defferent MARCHES for Volunteer Corps
Dedicated by Permission to LADY
St. Clair Erskine of Sinclair
BY
James Walker

Price _____ 4/

Printed for the Author and to be had at his house
in Dysart.___Sold also by Ja? JOHNSON
Music Seller Laws Market and at all
the other Dealers of Music,
EDINBURGH.

J. Johnson Sculp?

The Heather House

Slow

Variations

Lady St Clairs Erskine's Reel

Miss St Clair Erskine of Sinclair

Miss Sarjent Livingstons Reel

Lieut Morisons (Dumfries Militia) Reel

Miss Black's Reel

Sir James St Clair Erskine

Strathspey

Miss Fergus's Reel

40

Miss Wemyss of Cuttelhills

Strathspey

Miss Christie of Durrie

Reel

Mr Willm. Ferguson of Reaths Reel

Miss Melvel Dysart   Reel

British Tars can do it

Miss Sally McLean　　　an Irish Air

Slowish

Miss Ann Drysdales Kirkaldy Reel

43

Miss Williams, London

Miss Johnson Pitworth

Reel

Miss Smith, Berwick

Miss E Erskine   Strathspey

Liewt. Jamiesons Quick Step

Miss Scaffe, London

Mrs Lieut. Morisons fancy

Miss Thomson, London

Miss Oswald, Dunnikeer   Reel

46

Stornway Lassies

Miss Dorset, Begnor Park

Reel

Braes of Marr, with Variations

Miss Balfowr Balberny

Reel

Miss Isabella Heggie Kirkcaldy Reel

Fife Docks

Mr G Paterson's Reel

A Clarkson

Mr Andrew Thomsons Reel

50

Mr James Frasers Reel

A Clarkson

Miss M S Reddie's Reel

A Clarkson

Mr Sharps Reel

A Clarkson

Breechan Lasses

Stewart

52

Auchtertool Volunteers March

Auchtertool Volunteers Quick Step

Dysart Volunteers March

Dysart Volunteers Quick Step